THE WORLD OF

BOGART

THE WORLD OF

BY PETER PLANT

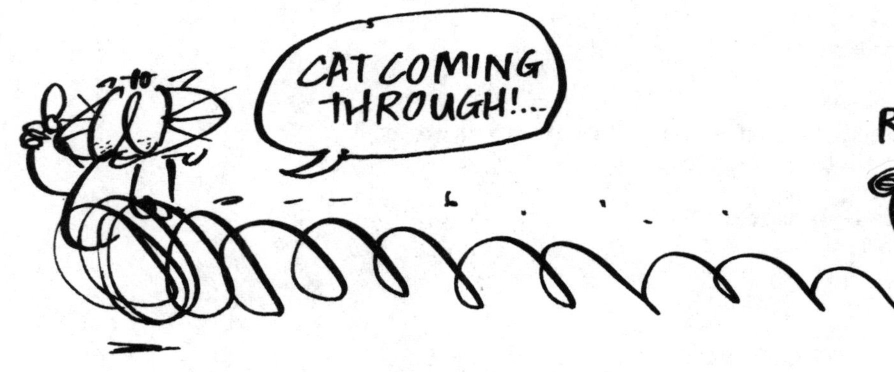

Robson Books

"REOWR. MREOWR. FSST. REOWRR."

Bogart Wilkins, July 1996

First published in Great Britain in 1996 by Robson Books Ltd, Bolsover House, 5-6 Clipstone Street, London W1P 8LE

British Library Cataloguing in Publication Data
A catalogue record for this title is available from the British Library

ISBN 1 86105 076 3

Printed by The Guernsey Press Company Limited, Guernsey, Channel Islands

YAAAGH! BOGART! THERE ARE TWO SPIDERS IN THE BATH!

STOMP ON THEM, BOGART! SQUELCH THEM! PULVERIZE THEM! KILL THEM!
MUMBLE
MUMBLE

THEY'RE MAKIN' LOVE, ROZ. YOU CAN'T KILL TWO SPIDERS WHEN THEY'RE MAKIN' LOVE.
PETER PLANT

OKAY, ROZ. I ADMIT HE'S A FAIRLY BIG SPIDER, BUT HE'S PROB'LY AS FRIENDLY AS A PUPPY!

HEY, BERNIE. TAKE A PEEK OVER THE WALL AND SEE IF PABLO THE DOG IS THERE, WILL YA?
OKAY.

YEAH. HE'S THERE.
PETER PLANT

POOR UNCLE NIGEL. HE WON A BLUE RIBBON AT THE EAST FERNLEA FLOWER SHOW AND THEN GOT DISQUALIFIED WHEN TRACES OF A BANNED SUBSTANCE WAS FOUND IN HIS SOIL.
TSK!

FUNNY. IT'S NOT LIKE UNCLE NIGE' TO TAKE ANYTHING OTHER THAN THE ODD DROP OF BABY BIO NOW AND THEN FOR MEDICINAL PURPOSES.
WHAT'S BEHIND IT?

PERSONALLY, I RECKON SOME OLD BIDDY DUMPED THE REMAINS OF A GIN AND TONIC INTO HIM AT THE OPENING FESTIVITIES.
AHA! IT WAS A 'PLANT'!
PETER PLANT

RRRRRR
TAXI!

CATS REALLY GO FOR THE TASTE OF FESTER'S CAT CHOW!...
HEY, THAT'S THE STUFF ROZ GOT ME!

...BECAUSE IT'S CHOCK FULL OF DEE-LICIOUS CHOPPED FISH HEADS AND RABBIT LIVERS...

...SMOTHERED IN A TANGY GRAVY OF PUREED PIG'S BLADDERS....

BOGART! YOU HAVEN'T TOUCHED YOUR DINNER!
PETER PLANT

BZAZ

FLANG

THAT'S THE THIRD ONE YOU'VE MISSED TODAY, QUINCE! ARE YA SURE YOU DON'T NEED GLASSES?
PETER PLANT

'A CAT FOR ALL SEASONS, BY BERNARD M. FACKELMYER. DEDICATED TO GERRY, A LOYAL FRIEND AND MASTER, WITHOUT WHOSE ASSISTANCE THIS BOOK WOULD NOT HAVE BEEN POSSIBLE.'

SAY, BERNIE. IF YA DON'T MIND MY SAYIN' SO, YOUR SPELLING ISN'T TOO HOT. WOULD YA LIKE SOME HELP?

HERE WE ARE IN EAST FERNLEA FLYERS' DRESSING ROOM WHERE THE MOOD IS SOMBRE AFTER A SEVEN-NIL LOSS TO WILLOWDEAN WANDERERS.

ONLY THE PURRING OF FIFTEEN HAIR DRYERS BREAKS THE SILENCE.
PURRRRRRR RRRRRRRR RRRRRRRR RRRRRRRR

PURRRRRRR RRRRRRR RRRRRRR RRRRRRR RRRRRRR RRRRRRR RRRRRRR RRRRRRR

IT WOULD BE SIXTEEN, BUT CHADWICK, FLYERS' GOALKEEPER, IS BALD.
HEY! WATCH WHERE YOU'RE POINTIN' THAT THING!
PETER PLANT

RICKSHAW!
RRRRRRRR

I SEE OLD MIKE IS HOME FROM HAVIN' HIS NEW PACEMAKER FITTED.

SNEAK
SNEAK
SNEAK

BOO!
EEEEEEE

I HATE MYSELF FOR DOING THAT BUT IT'S BEST TO TEST OUT THESE DEVICES SOONER RATHER THAN LATER.
POUND POUND POUND POUND POUND POUND POUND
PETER PLANT

DON'T YOU THINK IT'S A WEE BIT EARLY TO PUT THOSE LOBELIA IN, HENRY?

NONSENSE, EDNA. SPRING IS HERE! NOW HAND ME THAT TROWEL.

DIG
DIG
PLANT
PLANT

HENRY, IT'S-
I KNOW! I KNOW!
PETER PLANT

GAD! 5:55 IN THE MORNING IS A FINE TIME FOR HER TO TELL ME HER BOYFRIEND GETS BACK AT SIX!

THE DOG AND DUCK
THE DOG AND DUCK

THE DOG AND DUCK
THE DOG AND DUCK

GARRRRRRR
ARR SNAP SNAP ARRRR
RRRARRRRR
SNARRRLL
DOG AND DUCK

CHEE! I'D SURE HATE TO MEET THE DOG!
TOO RIGHT!

IF I DIVORCE MY OWNER, WHAT ARE MY RIGHTS?
CAT LAWYER

YOU CAN TAKE YOUR BED, YOUR FEEDING DISH, YOUR RUBBER MOUSE, YOUR COLLAR AND TAG, AND A BAG OF KITTY TREATS. THAT'S ABOUT IT....

SOME CATS LIKE TO TRY AND WANGLE A FEW VIDEO TAPES, OR THEIR FAVOURITE CD. BUT IT'S DIFFICULT.

CAN I GO FOR THE HOUSE?
WHEW! YES, BUT YOU'RE TALKING A HEFTY LEGAL FEE!
CAT LAWYER
PETER PLANT

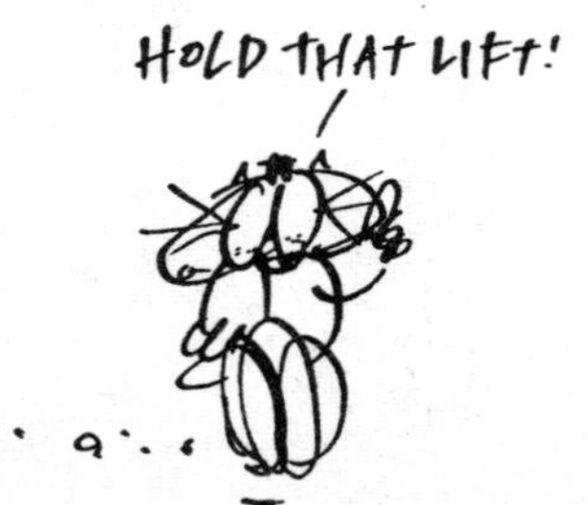
HOLD THAT LIFT!

CHEERS, ROZ. I'M OUTA HERE. THIS PLACE AN' ME ARE HISTORY. I'M OFF TO LIVE WITH MRS. HENDERSON...

BEST OF LUCK, OL' GIRL. I'M SURE YOU'LL FIND A NEW CAT. I'LL BE BACK TO PICK UP MY MAIL.

CLICK

YEAH HEY LISTEN IT LOOKS LIKE MRS. HENDERSON HAS GONE AWAY FOR THE WEEK SO I'LL HAFTA STAY HERE FOR A FEW DAYS...
SLAM
PETER PLANT

THE EAST FERNLEA FROG JUMPING CHAMPIONSHIPS ARE ONLY A WEEK AWAY, QUINCE! WE BETTER START PRACTISING.
RIBBIT

REMEMBER TO CONCENTRATE ON HEIGHT AND DISTANCE, GOT IT? HEIGHT AND DISTANCE.
READYYY... STEADYYY...

GO!
BAM!

OKAY, YOU'VE GOT THE HEIGHT, NOW LET'S GO FOR DISTANCE.
PETER PLANT

FROG-JUMPING
CHAMPIONSHIPS
REGISTRATION

RIBBIT
-JUMPING
MPIONSHIPS
GISTRATION
SCRIBBLE
SCRIBBLE

THANK YOU.
ISTRATION

WOULD YOU BELIEVE THAT WAS THE FORTY-SIXTH FROG IN A ROW WITH THE SAME NAME!
FROG-JUMPING
REGISTRATION

PLOP!...
EEEEEAGH!
EEEEEAGH!
EEAGH! EEAGH!
EEEEEEAGH!
SHAKESHAKE
SHAKESHAKE
THUMP THUMP
BEAT BEAT
HOP THUMP

WANNA HEAR THE FIRST CHAPTER OF MY NEW NOVEL, BOGART?
SHOOT, ERIC.

(AHEM) THE WARM SUMMER SUN BEAT DOWN UPON BRENDA THE BEGONIA. SHE KEPT THINKING ABOUT GERALD THE GERANIUM AND HOW SHE LONGED TO CROSS-POLLINATE WITH HIM. 'WHERE WAS BRAD THE BEE?' SHE SIGHED. 'IT'S NOT LIKE HIM TO BE THIS LATE.'

VERY, VERY NICE, ERIC.
IN CHAPTER TWO SHE FINDS OUT GERALD HAS GREENFLY.
PETER PLANT

OH, WISE LAMA, HOW DO I FIND INNER PEACE?
TO FIND INNER PEACE, MY SON, YOU MUST SIT AT THE FOOT OF THE TREE OF ETERNAL SOLITUDE.

HOW DO I FIND THE TREE OF ETERNAL SOLITUDE?
GO ALONG THE ROAD OF BLISS-FUL TRANQUILITY TILL YOU COME TO THE RIVER OF QUIET CONTENTMENT...

...GO OVER THE BRIDGE OF EUPHORIC HAPPINESS, ACROSS THE MEADOW OF RAPTUROUS FULFILMENT, THROUGH THE FOREST OF CELESTIAL REPOSE, UP THE HILL OF IDYLLIC-
OKAY... OKAY...
PETER PLANT

SSH! BABY'S ASLEEP!
RRR-OH! SORRY!

OH GREAT LAMA WHOSE WISDOM EXCEEDS THAT OF A THOUSAND KINGS, I COME SEEKING THE SECRET OF LIFE!

NOW IS NOT THE TIME TO SEEK THE SECRET OF LIFE, MY SON! GO, AND RETURN ON THE MORROW!

BUT I HAVE HEARD OF YOUR VAST AND WONDROUS KNOW-LEDGE, OH LAMA!...
NOW IS NOT THE TIME!

...AND OF YOUR GREAT VISION AND UNDER-STANDING-
LISTEN, I'M ACTUALLY **WITH** SOME-ONE.
PETER PLANT

NEVER FORGET THE GREAT CAT WAR OF '82. FOR SEVEN AND A HALF MONTHS, FELINE FOUGHT FELINE WITH AN INTENSITY BORDERING ON THE INSANE.

WHEN IT WAS OVER, THE ENTIRE CAT WORLD HEAVED A SIGH OF RELIEF, VOWING NEVER TO INFLICT SUCH TERRIBLE CARNAGE AND DEVASTATION ON ITSELF AGAIN.
GEE. WHAT STARTED IT ALL?

TOMMY CALLAGHAN CALLED CHARLIE McALLISTER A DICKHEAD.

HOLY COW! THE HOTPANTS THAT YOUNG LADY IS WEARING ARE EXTREMELY TIGHT!
STRUT STRUT STRUT STRUT STRUT STRUT STRUT

AS A MATTER OF FACT, THEY'RE THE TIGHTEST HOTPANTS I'VE EVER **SEEN**!
STRUT STRUT STRUT STRUT STRUT STRUT STRUT

OOPS! SHE DROPPED HER BUS PASS.... SHE'S BENDING OVER TO PICK IT U-
BLAM!

GOOD GRIEF! THEY EXPLODED!
PETER PLANT

I'M DEVASTATED, BOG! TO THINK MELANIE'S BEEN HAVIN' AN AFFAIR BEHIND MY BACK!
MAYBE IT'S ALL A BIG MISTAKE, BERNIE.

MISTAKE? BUT I SAW THEM (SOB) KISSIN' AN' CUDDLIN' TOGETHER LIKE A COUPLE OF LOV.... LOV.... OH, SOB HACK SOB SOB SOB SOB SOB HACK SOB SOB SOB SOB SNORK SOB SOB!
HEAVE WRACK HEAVE

SNIF

THIS MEANS YOU'RE GONNA WRECK THE NUMBERS AT MY BOWLING PARTY, DOESN'T IT.
PETER PLANT

BOG! BOG! MELANIE HAS COME BACK TO ME! SHE'S COME **BACK**!

LAST NIGHT SHE KNOCKED ON THE DOOR AN' TOLD ME SHE WAS A FOOL TO FALL FOR A GUY LIKE MICHAEL AN' ANYWAY SHE ALWAYS KNEW IT WAS ME SHE REALLY LOVED!!

SO WE KISSED AN' CUDDLED AN' LAY THERE IN EACH OTHER'S ARMS FOR A WHILE, HALF LAUGHING, HALF CRYING.

WHERE IS SHE NOW?
OH, RON, HER AEROBICS INSTRUCTOR, WANTED TO SHOW HER HIS NEW CYCLING SHORTS.
PETER PLANT

Y'KNOW WHAT I THINK, BERNIE? I THINK THIS 'AFFAIR' MELANIE YOUR GIRLFRIEND IS HAVING IS JUST A TEMPORARY INFATUATION.

A TEMPORARY INFATUATION WITH SOME BIG HAIRY BRUTE WHO HAPPENS TO BE NOT-BAD-LOOKING AND LAYS CLAIM TO A BIT OF SEX APPEAL.

SOME BEEFY BOZOO WHO LOOKS AT HER WITH DARK, PENETRATIN' EYES THAT SAY 'I WANT YOU, MELANIE.... I WANT YOU'....

SOME MACHO LOVER-BOY WHO-
AWRIGHT! AWRIGHT!
SORRY.
PETER PLANT

RRRRRRR
BANDITS AT TWO O'CLOCK!
BRRRRRR...
TATATATA TATATA TATATA TATATATAT

WHAT DID YOU DO IN THE GREAT CAT WAR OF '82, MIKE?

I WAS SECOND-IN-COMMAND OF C-SECTION OF THE ELITE LATERAL COMBAT UNIT RESPONSIBLE FOR TACTICAL FALLBACK DETERRENCE DURING ENEMY COUNTER-STRIKE OFFENSIVES.

GEE. WHAT DOES THAT MEAN?
ABSOLUTELY NO IDEA.
PETER PLANT

I WONDER IF OL' QUINCY, HERE, IS ACTUALLY A PRINCE CAST UNDER A WITCH'S EVIL SPELL.

WE'LL HAFTA FIND SOMEONE WHO'LL **KISS** HIM. HMMM... LET'S SEEE...
I KNOW! COME ON, BIG FELLA!
PETER PLANT

A LITTLE LATER...
LISTEN, I DO BIRTHDAY PARTIES AND STAG DO'S. FROGS ARE DEFINITELY A NO-NO.
KATHY'S KISS-A GRAMS

INFORMED THAT QUINCY MAY ACTUALLY BE A HANDSOME PRINCE, ANGELA SMECKLESBY, A POPULAR LOCAL GIRL, ATTEMPTS TO FIND OUT.

OBOY!

KISS

OH WISE AND FRUITFUL LAMA WHO KNOWS ALL THINGS, WHAT IS THE SECRET OF LIFE?

THE SECRET OF LIFE, MY SON, IS.... 'THE WET BIRD WHO FLIES IN THE SUN SHALL HAVE CURLY FEATHERS'

HOW CAN I THANK YOU, OH LAMA? FOR I HAVE BEEN TRULY ENLIGHTENED!
PETER PLANT

IF YOU'RE GOING PAST DINKY'S SANDWICH BAR GRAB US A TUNA FISH AND MAYO ON BROWN.

YAHoo!
BLAM
BLAM
RRKRARRRR

LET'S MAKE A FINAL CHECK FOR THE BROTHERHOOD'S ANNUAL SUMMER BARBECUE TONIGHT.
RIGHT.

WHO'S RESPONSIBLE FOR THE MUSIC?
BROTHER HENDERSON.
WHO'S DOING THE BURGERS?
BROTHER FENCHUCK.
WHO'S BEHIND THE BAR?
BROTHER QUIGLEY.

AND WHO'S MAKING SURE BABS FARNWELLER DOESN'T HAVE TOO MUCH TO DRINK AND START GETTING RANDY?
NOBODY.
GOOD.
PETER PLANT

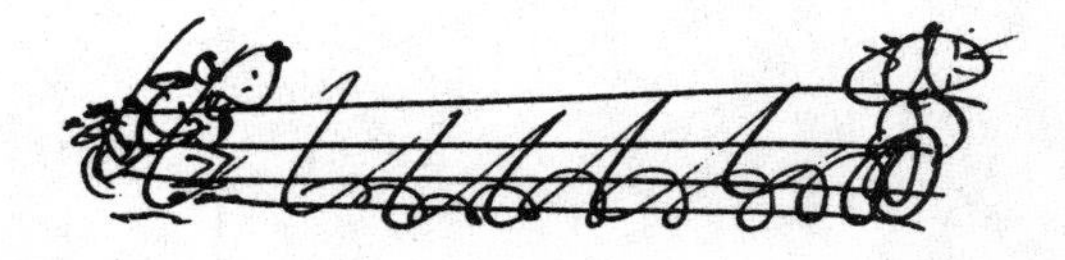

AHH! It's SUMMER, BERNIE. AN' SUMMER IS THE MATIN' SEASON.

GEE, IS THAT RIGHT, BOG'? I ALWAYS THOUGHT **SPRING** WAS THE MATIN' SEASON.
OH, YES. SPRING IS A MATIN' SEASON. NO DOUBT ABOUT IT.

AND HOW ABOUT AUTUMN?
AUTUMN, TOO, IS A MATIN' SEASON.
WINTER?
MATIN' SEASON.

IS THERE ANY TIME WHEN IT **ISN'T** THE MATIN' SEASON?
THE MONDAY BEFORE PASSOVER IS CONSIDERED TO BE A DAY OF REST.
PETER PLANT

BOGART TRAINS A NEW RECRUIT FOR HIS SKY-DIVING TEAM.
FREE FALL TILL YOU COUNT TEN THEN YANK YOUR CORD.
LEAP
ONE.... TWO....
THREE.... FOUR.... FIVE.... SIX....
SEVEN.... EIGHT.... NINE.... T-
BAM!
BETTER MAKE THAT NINE AN' YANK.

THE EAST FERNLEA ALL-CAT SKY DIVING TEAM WERE A CLOSE-KNIT GROUP.
YO!
EF
EF
EF

HERE'S YOUR 'CHUTE, OL' PAL. I PACKED IT FOR YA.
AW, CHEERS, OL' CHUM!

HAVE A GOOD DIVE, BUDDY!
THANKS, MATE.
OH, AND BY THE WAY, OL' COBBER.
WHAT'S THAT, AMIGO?

I KNOW WHAT'S BEEN GOING ON BETWEEN YOU AND MY MAUREEN.
PETER PLANT

A PRE-PRACTICE MEETING OF THE EAST FERNLEA ALL-CAT SKY-DIVING DISPLAY TEAM.
ER, LISTEN, GUYS. ABOUT THIS NEW ROUTINE WE'RE WORKING ON.
WHAT ABOUT IT, DAVE?

WHEN WE'RE FREE-FALLING IN THE GIANT THREE-POINT STAR...
YEAH?

DO WE HAVE TO HOLD HANDS?
PETER PLANT

A PRACTISE SESSION OF THE EAST FERNLEA ALL-CAT SKY-DIVING DISPLAY TEAM
OI, RUTHERFORD! ON THIS TEAM NO ONE IS SPECIAL!
PETER PLANT

BLAST

NEVER FORGET THE DAY DURING THE GREAT CAT WAR OF '82, WHEN WE HAD TO CAPTURE A PIECE OF HIGH GROUND CALLED 'HILL FORTY-FOUR'!....

SARGE TOLD US THIS WOULD BE THE CRUCIAL BATTLE OF THE CAMPAIGN AND OUR ULTIMATE TEST AS A FIGHTING MACHINE! IF WE TOOK HILL FORTY-FOUR IT WOULD BE REMEMBERED AS C-COMPANY'S FINEST HOUR!

GOSH-DIDJA TAKE IT?
NAW. WE NEVER DID.
PETER PLANT

STOOPID CAT THINKS HE'S THE ONLY ONE WHO CAN RUN ON TWO LEGS!

SOMEONE CAME IN TODAY WHO WOULD HAVE BEEN PERFECT FOR YOU, SIR.
REALLY?
CATLINE DATING AGENCY

SHE WAS GORGEOUS! AB-SO-LUTE-LY GORGEOUS! LOVELY DARK EYES... BEAUTIFUL SOFT FUR.... AND WOULD YOU BELIEVE SHE LISTED HER INTERESTS AS 'GOING ON SEXY PICNICS' AND 'CUDDLING IN FRONT OF THE FIRE'?
WOW! SO WHAT HAPPENED TO HER??

I DECIDED TO TAKE HER OUT MYSELF.
CATLIN DATIN AGENC
PETER PLANT

RRRRRRRRR

HOW THE FIGHT BROKE OUT AT BOGART'S BROTHER'S WEDDING.
PST. THE FRIENDS OF THE BRIDE SAY THE FRIENDS OF THE GROOM ARE A LOAD OF SOFT-BELLIES.
PETER PLANT

WILL YOU SHOW ME HOW TO MEET GIRLS, BOG'?
SURE, BERNIE. SEE THAT LITTLE NUMBER OVER THERE?

ER... THAT'S A BIT OF A SEXIST EXPRESSION BOG'... 'LITTLE NUMBER'.
SORRY. SEE THAT 'YOUNG FELINE' WITH THE BODY THAT WON'T QUIT?

'BODY THAT WON'T QUIT' IS A BIT DEGRADING, ISN'T IT, BOG'?
OKAY. OKAY. THE CHICK WITH THE 'NICE FIGURE'.

ER, 'CHICK', BOG'–
LISTEN, DO YA WANNA MEET A BABE OR DO YA WANNA JOIN THE FEMINIST MOVEMENT?
PETER PLANT

I'M REALLY IN THE DOG-HOUSE WITH GERRY, BOG!
WHAT HAPPENED, BERNIE?

LAST NIGHT HE AND HIS NEW GIRLFRIEND WERE SITTIN' IN THE FRONT ROOM WITH THE LIGHTS DIMMED LISTENING TO FRANK SINATRA. I DECIDED TO GO IN AND SAY HELLO...

THAT'S WHEN ALL HELL BROKE LOOSE.

ALLERGIC TO CATS, WAS SHE?
SHE WAS STILL POWER-SNEEZING WHEN THE CAB ARRIVED!
PETER PLANT

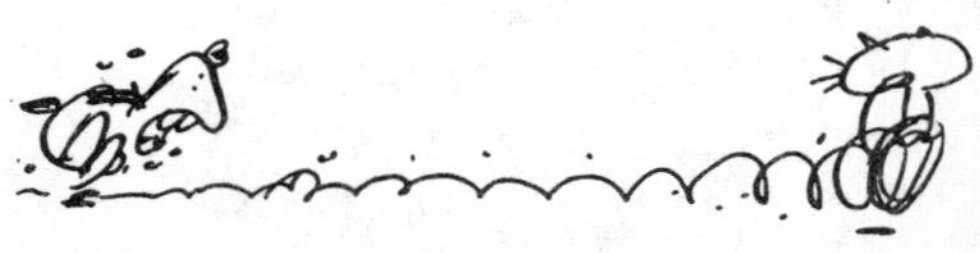
WOO WOO!

BROTHERS!...BROTHER FACKELMYER, OUR SOCIAL CONVENOR, HAS JUST INFORMED ME THAT TINA TURNER HAS **ACCEPTED** THE INVITATION TO PERFORM AT OUR ANNUAL SPRING 'HOP'!
YAAA!
HURRAAAY!
HOO-WEE!
CLAP CLAP CLAP

DO YOU MEAN TINA TURNER THE ROCK SINGER OR TINA, THE TURNERS' CAT?

GOOD GRIEF! I DIDN'T KNOW THERE'S A TINA TURNER WHO'S A ROCK SINGER!.
ME NEITHER!
PETER PLANT

NEVER FORGET THE DAY THE GREAT CAT WAR OF '82 ENDED. AFTER MONTHS OF FIGHTING THERE WAS REJOICING IN THE STREETS.

AS OUR PLATOON HEADED HOME, TIRED BUT HAPPY, SOME PRETTY YOUNG THINGS RAN UP AND KISSED US SMACK ON THE MOUTH WHILE THEIR BOYFRIENDS LOOKED ON...

WHICH WAS WHEN THE GREAT CAT WAR OF '83 BEGAN.
PETER PLANT

QUIETLY ENSCONCED IN OUR 'HIDE' HERE ON THE EDGE OF THE WAGAZANEEZI PLAIN...

...WE OBSERVE THE VIOLENT YET STRANGELY GRACEFUL MOVEMENTS OF A PAIR OF ADULT KDANGABEEST...

...AS THEY PERFORM THEIR EXOTIC MATING RIT—
GALLUMP
GALLUMP
GALLUMP
GALLUMP
GALLUMP
SMASH!
AAIEEEEEEE!!

I GUESS HE DIDN'T SEE THAT RHINO.
PETER PLANT

RRRRRR

AAAAGH! MY WHITES HAVE GONE DARK BLUE!!
CHUG CHUG CHUG

A DARK BLUE SOCK! THERE'S A DARK BLUE SOCK IN WITH THEM!!

HOW IN THE WORLD COULD A DARK BLUE SOCK GET IN WITH MY WHITES?
PETER PLANT

HANG ON, HERE! ARE YOU TALKING ABOUT THE DARK BLUE SOCK I FOUND BESIDE YOUR LAUNDRY BASKET THIS MORNING?
WAAAAAAAAA

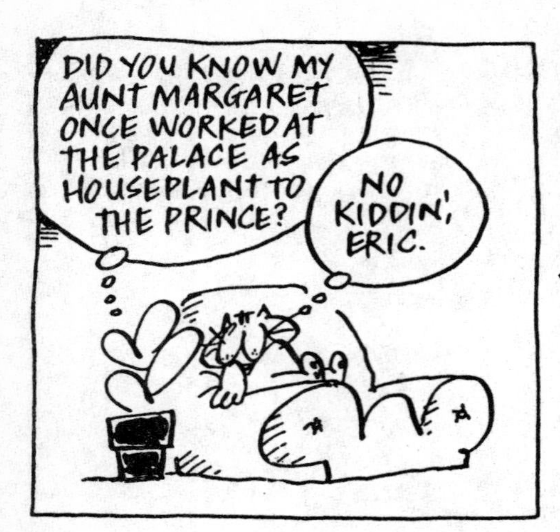
DID YOU KNOW MY AUNT MARGARET ONCE WORKED AT THE PALACE AS HOUSEPLANT TO THE PRINCE?
NO KIDDIN', ERIC.

YEAH. FOR SEVEN YEARS SHE SAT ON HIS BEDSIDE TABLE LISTENING TO HIM TALK TO HER ABOUT HIS IDEAS, HIS PROBLEMS, HIS HOPES AND DREAMS. THEN, ONE NIGHT, SHE DIED.
GOSH. WHAT HAPPENED?

THE PRINCE HAD FALLEN ASLEEP AFTER A HOT CURRY AND FORGOTTEN TO OPEN THE WINDOW.
TSK.
PETER PLANT

DOING DOING DOING

SQUISH

YAAAAAAGH!

I SAID GO AND HIBERNATE IN THE CELLAR, NOT THE WELLY, QUINCE! YOU'RE LUCKY YOU WEREN'T KILLED!
PETER PLANT

THAT GIRL YOU INTRODUCED ME TO WHO LIKES TO 'PARTY' SEVEN NIGHTS A WEEK FELL ASLEEP ON ME!!
CATLINE DATING AGENCY

HMMMMM....
AH...
CATLINE DATING AGENCY

UNFORTUNATELY YOU GOT HER ON THE SEVENTH NIGHT, SIR.
CATLINE DATING AGENCY
PETER PLANT

BROTHER BEAVERS, IT IS WITH GREAT SADNESS THAT I INFORM YOU OF THE DEATH OF OUR BELOVED BROTHER FENCHUCK, WHO PASSED AWAY PEACEFULLY IN HIS SLEEP ON SUNDAY MORNING.
PETER PLANT
SNIF
HACK
SOB
SNIF
SOB

ACTUALLY, IT WAS ON SATURDAY NIGHT, HE HAD FOUR GIRLS WITH HIM, AND IT WAS ANYTHING BUT PEACEFUL!
HURRAY!
ATTA BOY, MIKEY!
WOO-WOO!
PUNCH
PUNCH

CLICKITTY CLACK
CLICKITTY CLACK
CLICKITTY CLACK
HONNK!

BROTHER BEAVERS, DUE TO THE DEPARTURE OF BROTHER FENCHUCK, MEMBERSHIP IN THE ORDER IS OPEN.

I THEREFORE PUT BEFORE YOU FOR THE VOTE, THE FIRST APPLICANT, TIMOTHY SMECKLESFIELD! HOW SAY YE ALL?

BLAAGH!
PTOO!
YECH!
BLUGH!
HUEE!
HISSS!

WELL, TIM, AS YOU KNOW, OUR ELECTORAL SYSTEM IS CRUDE, BUT EFFECTIVE...
PETER PLANT

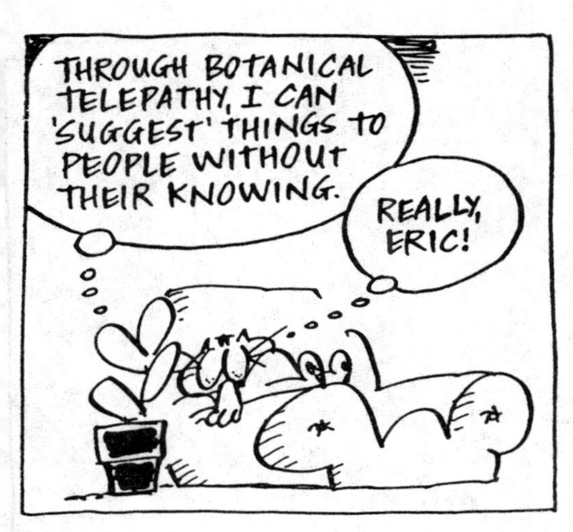
THROUGH BOTANICAL TELEPATHY, I CAN 'SUGGEST' THINGS TO PEOPLE WITHOUT THEIR KNOWING.
REALLY, ERIC!

YEAH. LIKE F'RINSTANCE YESTERDAY I GOT ROZ TO SWITCH CHANNELS ON THE TV. AND THE DAY BEFORE THAT I PERSUADED HER TO WASH HER HAIR.

SAY, YOU COULDN'T GET HER TO THROW OUT HER JULIO IGLESIAS ALBUMS, COULD YA?
PETER PLANT

THAT'S A VERY NICE NEW CAR MR. McILDUFFY HAS THERE.
VERY NICE.

BEAUTIFUL SHINY FINISH.
STAN 1

REALLY SUPERB SUSPENSION.
IRNK
IRNK
IRNK

ALARM'S A BIT LOUD.
CAN'T HAVE EVERYTHING.
BWEEW
BWEEW
BWEEW
BWEEW
BWEEW
BWEEW
PETER PLANT

RRRRRRR
THRUST
THRUST
THRUST
THRUST
THRUS

(SIGH) WE'RE NEVER GONNA BLOOMIN' GET ACROSS HERE!..
KZAZ
KZAZ
KZAZ
KZAZ

NEVER BLOOMIN' EVER...
KZAZ
BEEEEP
HONK
KZIZ

BERNIE! THERE! NOW! QUICK!
WHERE? WHEN? Y'MEAN GO FOR IT???
KZIZ
KZAZ
KZOOZ
KZOOZ
PETER PLANT

NO. I JUST SAW A '57 CHEVY.
KZAZ
KZIZ
ROAR
KZOOZ

...FOUR EGGS, A TABLESPOON OF GUAVA EXTRACT, AND A HALF PINT OF GOAT'S MILK...

...ADD FOUR SESAME SEEDS AND BEAT UNTIL SMOOTH AND FROTHY...

BEATBEATBEATBEAT
BEATBEATBEATBEAT
BEATBEATBEATBEAT
BEATBEATBEATBEAT
BEATBEATBEATBEAT
BEATBEATBEATBEAT
BEATBEATBEATBEAT
BEATBEATBEATBEAT
BEATBEATBEAT
BEATBEATBEAT

I'D SWITCH CHANNELS BUT THE STUPID REMOTE CONTROL IS WAY UP THERE ON TOP OF THE TV.
BEAT
BEAT
BEAT
BEAT
PETER PLANT

RUN
RUN
RUN
RUN
RUN
BOWL
CRICKET TODAY 1:30 P.M.

CRACK!
WHAP
CRICKET TODAY 1:30 P.M.

KEAZ
PETERPLANT

PERSONALLY, I WOULDN'T HAVE TRIED TO CATCH IT.
OR AT LEAST'VE LET IT BOUNCE ONCE OR TWICE.

RRRRRRRRR

WE HAD A FIRE IN THE KITCHEN LAST NIGHT.
NO KIDDIN', BERNIE!

YEAH. I QUICKLY GRABBED A WET TEA TOWEL, JUMPED UP ON THE COUNTER, AND BEAT OUT THE FLAMES.
GOOD THINKIN'.

THAT'S WHEN GERRY WHACKED ME.
WHAT FOR?

I'M NOT ALLOWED ON THE COUNTER.
PETERPLANT

BROTHER BEAVERS! OUR ANTI-SMOKING CAMPAIGN APPEARS TO HAVE BEEN A TREMENDOUS SUCCESS!
LOYAL ORDER OF
ELUSIVE BEAVERS

AS I LOOK OUT AMONG YOU I SEE NO ONE WITH A CIGARETTE IN HIS HAND!

CONGRATULATIONS TO EVERYONE WHO MADE THE 'SUPREME EFFORT' AND I NOW DECLARE 'STOP SMOKING WEEK' OFFICIALLY OVER!
CRASH

FLICK
FLICK
PUFFFFF
STRIKE
PUFF
PUFF
FLICK
SUCK
PUFF
STRIKE
STRIKE
PUFF
PUFFF
PUFF
PAFF
FLICK
SUCKKKKK
PUFF
KAFF
STRIKE
STRIKE
STRIKE
PETER PLANT

WOW! THIS IS A STEEP ONE!
PETER PLANT

MEANWHILE...
HAPPY BIRTHDAY TOOO YOOO,
HAPPY BIRTHDAY TOOO YOOO,
HAPPY BIRTH-DAYY DEAR
GRAAAN-DAAAD.....
HAPPY BIRTHDAY TOOOO...

KZAZ

THAT'S RIGHT! MESSERSCHMITTS! ABOUT FIFTY OF THEM!!

I FOUND HAIRS ON MY PILLOW THIS MORNIN', BOG! I THINK I'M GOIN' BALD!

IT MUST BE ON ACCOUNT OF THE WORRYIN'. LET'S FACE IT. I'M A CONSTANT WORRIER. WORRY, WORRY, WORRY, WORRY.

WHAT DO YA WORRY ABOUT?
GOIN' BALD.
PETER PLANT

SQUEEK!
YAGH!
PETER PLANT

WHY WAS YOUR RUBBER MOUSE STUFFED IN THE CASSETTE PLAYER?
I THOUGHT IT WOULD MAKE A NICE LITTLE HOUSE FOR HIM.

RRRRRRR

HOW THE SHOWDOWN WITH BOGART WENT DISASTEROUSLY WRONG FOR 'CAT' MANDOO.
HAW HAW! YOU THINK I'M GONNA FALL FOR THE OL' 'WATCH-OUT-FOR-THE-RUNAWAY-HOT-DOG-STAND' TRICK, EH?
HOT DOGS HOT DOGS
MIKE'S GIANT SUPER DOGS
KETCHUP
PETER PLANT

GETTING A DATE WITH NAOMI BERGERBUN IS **EASY**, GEOFF! ALL YOU DO IS PHONE HER UP AND SAY 'YO, NAOMI! IT'S GEOFF, HERE! HOW ABOUT A **DATE**?'

ALTHOUGH GROVER, THE PUB DOG HERE AT THE 'DOG AND DUCK', IS NOT AS FIT AS HE USED TO BE...
WHEEZ
HE IS ALWAYS READY TO SPRING INTO ACTION, IN CASE ANYONE...
PLOP!
PETER PLANT
DROPS SOME FOOD.

THE MICE AT THE 'DOG AND DUCK' CALLED A MEETING TODAY TO DECIDE WHAT TO DO ABOUT SAMSON, THE LANDLORD'S CAT.

RODNEY-THE-DEFIANT SAID THEY SHOULD THROW BEER MUGS AT HIM. DEREK-THE-CAUTIOUS SAID ONE OF THEM SHOULD ALWAYS STAND WATCH...

BUT WHEN LAWRENCE-THE-WISE SUGGESTED PUTTING A BELL AROUND THE CAT'S NECK, EVERYONE APPLAUDED.

THEN JEREMY-THE-CURIOUS ASKED WHO WOULD BE THE ONE TO PUT THE BELL ON THE CAT...
P.P.

AND AS EVERYONE STARTED CHANTING 'RICKY-THE-BRAVE... RICKY-THE-BRAVE...' RICK DUCKED OUT OF THE MEETING, DIDN'T YA, RICK!
SQUIRK

THE MICE DOWN AT THE DOG AND DUCK HAVE ASSIGNED RICK, HERE, THE TASK OF TYING A **BELL** AROUND THE NECK OF THE LANDLORD'S CAT...

I TOLD RICK THE BEST WAY TO ACCOMPLISH THIS WAS TO WAIT TILL THE CAT WAS ASLEEP, THROW THE RIBBON ON THE BELL **OVER** THE CAT, THEN TIE A DOUBLE REEF KNOT.

P.P.

A REEF KNOT IS LEFT OVER RIGHT THEN RIGHT OVER– LISTEN, RICK, WHY DON'TCHA JUST GO BACK AND TELL THEM YOU'VE GOT A TUMMY ACHE, HM?

HOW DID THE MISSION TO TIE A BELL ON THE CAT AT THE DOG AND DUCK GO LAST NIGHT, RICK?
SQUEEK SQUEEK SQUEEK SQUEEK SQUEEK SQUEEK SQUEEK SQUEEK SQUEEK.

AFTER ASCERTAINING THAT THE TARGET WAS ASLEEP, YOU ADVANCED TO WITHIN APPROXIMATELY TWO AND A HALF INCHES FROM IT. THEN WHAT?
SQUEEK SQUEEK SQUEEK.

YOU DECIDED TO ABORT? BUT WHY?
SQUEEK SQUEEK SQUEEK.
PETER PLANT

AH. I SEE. THE TARGET WOKE UP.
SQUIRK.

RRRRRRR
ROARRR

OOH! A HARLEY

THREE THINGS CAT-OWNERS OFTEN DO THAT ANNOY THEIR CATS
1. TALK BABY-TALK TO THEM.
WHO'S A PRIT-TEE IDDY-BIDDY-WIDDY PUDDY, THEN?
2. SHOW THEM HOLIDAY SNAPS.
...HERE'S ANOTHER ONE OF ROGER AND ME AT BARNACLE BAY...
YAWN
3. CALL THEM 'FUSSY'!
I'M NOT FUSSY! THIS STUFF IS CRUD!
GARt
PETER PLANT

TAKE IT FROM ME. THE ONLY WAY TO BEAT YOUR STINT IN THIS PLACE IS TO TAKE IT ONE DAY AT A TIME. IF YOU START THINKIN' AHEAD ABOUT THE DAY YOU GET 'SPRUNG' YOU'LL GO CRAZY...
COLDITCH CATTERY
EAST COMPOUND

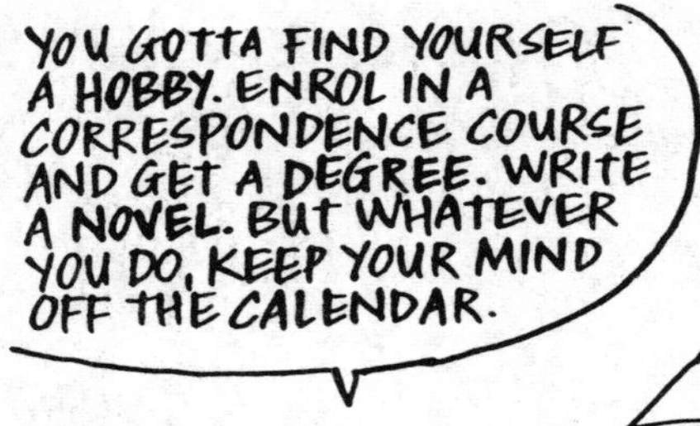
YOU GOTTA FIND YOURSELF A HOBBY. ENROL IN A CORRESPONDENCE COURSE AND GET A DEGREE. WRITE A NOVEL. BUT WHATEVER YOU DO, KEEP YOUR MIND OFF THE CALENDAR.

THANKS FOR THE TIP. HOW LONG ARE YOU IN FOR?
TILL TUESDAY. HOW ABOUT YOU?
MONDAY, NOON.
PETER PLANT

THERE ARE TWO GUARDS IN THIS PLACE. MRS. KAZNOWSKI WHO IS MEAN, RUTHLESS AND SADISTIC, AND MISS ABERTHWAITE WHO IS SOFTER AND MORE LENIENT.
COLDITCH CATTERY
EAST COMPOUND

OI! HENDERSON! SIX DAYS IN 'SOLITARY' FOR HAVIN' A FUNNY LOOK ON YER FACE!!
SLAM!
CLICK.

WHO WAS THAT?
MISS ABERTHWAITE.
PETER PLANT

SO THAT'S MRS. KAZNOWSKI.
YEP. THAT'S HER.
COLDITCH CATTERY
EAST COMPOUND
TAP TAP

UNBELIEVABLE! SIMPLY UN-BELIEVABLE!
YEAH. SHE'S PRETTY SCARY, ALL RIGHT.

NO, I MEAN SHE'S ACTUALLY MARRIED!
HENDERSON! FRONT-AN'-CENTRE! NOW!
PETER PLANT

PSST!... MIKE!.... I DUG A TUNNEL! IT GOES FROM HERE TO THE FEMALE SECTION. ARE YA WITH ME?
COLDITCH CATTERY
EAST COMPOUND

WHY DIDJA DIG A TUNNEL INTO THE FEMALE SECTION?

BECAUSE THERE ARE FEMALES THERE, YA LUNK-HEAD!
PETER PLANT

CHOPPACHOPPACHOPPA

CHOPPACHOPPACHOPPA
RRRRRRR

MAIL-CALL AT THE CATTERY WAS ANOTHER OPPORTUNITY FOR MRS. KAZNOWSKI TO REVEAL HER CRUEL SENSE OF HUMOUR.
HERE'S ONE FOR BOGART WILKINS....'TO MY LITTLE BOGIE-POOS. HAVING A LOVELY TIME. MISS YOU. LOVE, ROZZIE.' HAW HAW HAW! 'BOGIE-POOS'!
I'LL GET YOU FOR THIS.
MAIL
PETER PLANT

(SIGH) I JUST HAD A VISIT FROM MY GIRLFRIEND, RITA. SHE SAYS SHE'S 'MET SOMEONE' AND WANTS TO 'GO' WITH HIM.
TSK.
COLDITCH CATTERY
EAST COMPOUND

I CAN'T SAY I BLAME HER. SHE'S A YOUNG, VIVACIOUS FELINE WITH NEEDS AND DESIRES. I HAD HOPED SHE'D WAIT FOR ME BUT I GUESS, IN THE END, WAITING WAS TOO HARD.

GEE. HOW LONG HAVE YOU BEEN 'INSIDE'?
ABOUT HALF AN HOUR.
PETER PLANT

I'VE COME TO PICK UP BOGART.
AH, BOGART. HE'S BEEN PUT IN 'SOLITARY'.
COLDITCH CATTERY
RECEPTION

'SOLITARY'? BUT WHY?
BECAUSE ON SATURDAY NIGHT HE STOLE THE MASTER KEY FROM MRS. QUIGLEY'S DESK AND THREW A PARTY IN THE FEMALE SECTION.

G-GOSH! DID.... ANYTHING...

I DON'T SUPPOSE THERE'S ANY CHANCE THE LITTLE FELLOW'S BEEN NEUTERED.
ER... NO... I HAVEN'T-
DIDN'T THINK SO.
PETER PLANT

UNCLE BOGART, WHAT IS 'SAFE SEX'?
NOT DOING IT ON TOP OF AN OLD DUSTBIN IN A HIGH WIND.

OH, WISE LAMA... WHAT IS THE SECRET OF LIFE?
CLICK...

(SIGH) HE WHO CLIMBS TO THE SUMMIT OF THE MOUNTAIN SHALL HAVE THE BEST VIEW OF THE VALLEY!
CLICK

A THOUSAND THANKS, OH LEARNED ONE.
DON'T MENTION IT.
CLICK

OH RATS! YOU MADE ME DROP MY TOENAIL CLIPPERS!
PETER PLANT

BOGART LOOKS UP AN OLD FRIEND HE SPENT TIME IN THE CATTERY WITH.
AW, IT'S GREAT TO SEE YA, OL' MATE! SAY, REMEMBER I TOLDJA ABOUT MY SISTER, MARIA? WELL SHE'S DYIN' TO MEETCHA!
PETER PLANT

RRRRRRRR

HAS BOGART BEEN ANNOYING YOU, TONY?
NOT AT ALL, ROZ! IN FACT, WE'VE BEEN HAVING A NICE LITTLE CHAT...

...HAVEN'T WE, BOGIE?
MEOW!
MEOW!

SEE?
MEOW MEOW!
MEOW MEOW!
P.P.

MEOW MEOW MEOW!
MEOW MEOW MEOW!
WHAT A KLUTZ!

AT THE EAST FERNLEA ALL-CAT SKY-DIVING CHAMPIONSHIPS
LEAP
HERE COMES 'SKYCAT' HARRIS!
JUDGES

WOW! A TRIPLE BACKWARD 'TUCK' ROLL FOLLOWED BY A REVERSE LATERAL SPEED-SPIN BREAKING INTO A DOUBLE INVERTED 'EAGLE'!

BRAVO!
HURRAYYY!
BUMP
CLAPCLAPCLAP CLAPCLAPCLAP CLAPCLAPCLAP CLAPCLAPCLAP
10
10
10
10
4
JUDGES
PETER PLANT

FOUR?? YOU GAVE HIM A LOUSY FOUR?
I THOUGHT HE WAS SHOWING OFF.
10
10
4

STILL AT THE EAST FERNLEA ALL-CAT SKY-DIVING CHAMPIONSHIPS
JUDGES

JUDGES

FLIP
8
JUDGES

ER, EVEN THOUGH HIS 'CHUTE DIDN'T OPEN I THOUGHT IT WAS A NICE DIVE.
8
JUDGES
PETER PLANT

BUMP
YELP!

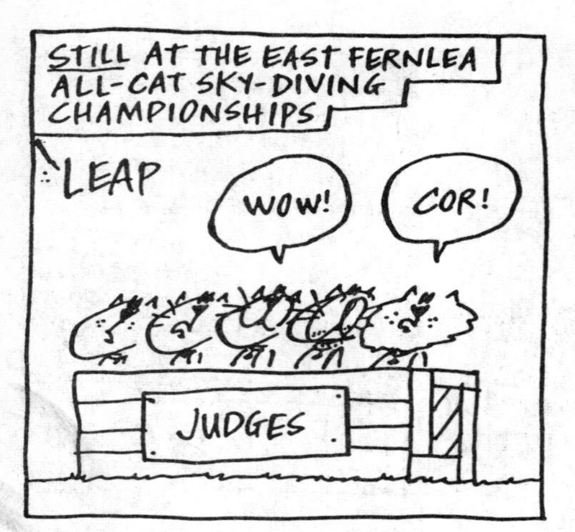
STILL AT THE EAST FERNLEA ALL-CAT SKY-DIVING CHAMPIONSHIPS
LEAP
WOW!
COR!
JUDGES

REMEMBER, LADS. WE'RE TOTALLY IMPARTIAL. WE MUSTN'T LET THE FACT THAT SHE IS A BEAUTIFUL FELINE WITH A STUNNING BODY INFLUENCE OUR SCORING.
SOARRRRR
HEAR HEAR.
JUDGES

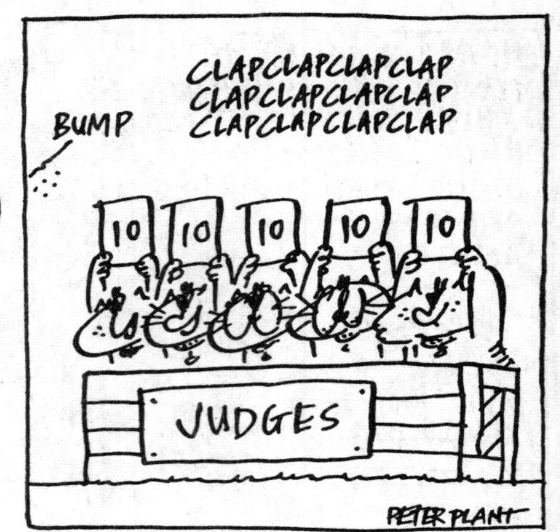
BUMP
CLAPCLAPCLAPCLAP
CLAPCLAPCLAPCLAP
CLAPCLAPCLAPCLAP
10
10
10
10
10
JUDGES
PETER PLANT

HERE WE ARE AT THE TENNIS CHAMPIONSHIPS WHERE, DESPITE TORN KNEE LIGAMENTS, A DISLOCATED SHOULDER, AND A SPRAINED ANKLE....
DASH DASH DASH DASH
LEAP

PETE 'HEADBAND' SMEDHURST, THE NUMBER ELEVEN SEED, IS PUTTING ON AN INCREDIBLE DISPLAY OF WILL AND STAMINA...
SPRINT SPRINT SPRINT SPRINT
LUNGE

AS HE RACES BACK AND FORTH ACROSS THE COURT...
SCRAMBLE SCRAMBLE SCRAMBLE SCRAMBLE
DIVE

ASKING EVERY SINGLE GIRL IN THE PLACE FOR HER PHONE NUMBER.
PUFF PANT GASP WHEEZ ...AND (GASP) HAVE YOU GOT A FAX?
PETER PLANT

HERE AT THE TENNIS CHAMPIONSHIPS, THE CROWD GOES SILENT AS, ONCE AGAIN, THE UMPIRE LEANS TOWARD THE MICROPHONE TO SPEAK.
AHEM

ADVANTAGE IVAN.... ER.... ADVANTAGE IVANN...UM... ADVANTAGE IVANNN.... .... ER......

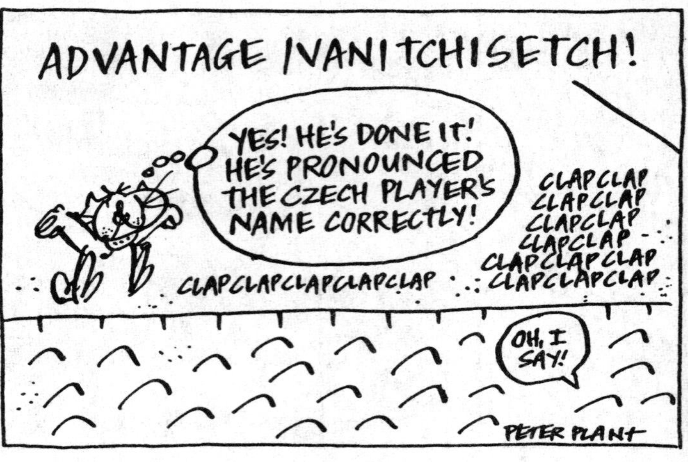
ADVANTAGE IVANITCHISETCH!
YES! HE'S DONE IT! HE'S PRONOUNCED THE CZECH PLAYER'S NAME CORRECTLY!
CLAPCLAP CLAPCLAP CLAPCLAP CLAPCLAP CLAPCLAPCLAP CLAPCLAPCLAP
CLAPCLAPCLAPCLAPCLAP
OH, I SAY!
PETER PLANT

ENTRANCE
UH-OHHH..

'MAC' MACINTOSH MAY NOT BE QUITE THE PLAYER HE USED TO BE, BUT HE STILL KNOWS HOW TO KEEP THE CROWD AMUSED.
MACINTOSH
HICKSFORD
...SO THE BALL BOY SAYS TO THE GUY, 'SORRY ABOUT THE MUSTARD, GUV', WE'VE ALL HAD HOT DOGS FOR LUNCH'!
HAHAHAHA
HAHAHAHAHAHAHAHAHA
HAHAHAHA
HAHA HAHAHA
HAHAHA HAHAHAHA
HAHAHAHAHAHAHAHAHAHA
HAHAHAHAHA
HAHAHAHA HAHAHA
PETER PLANT

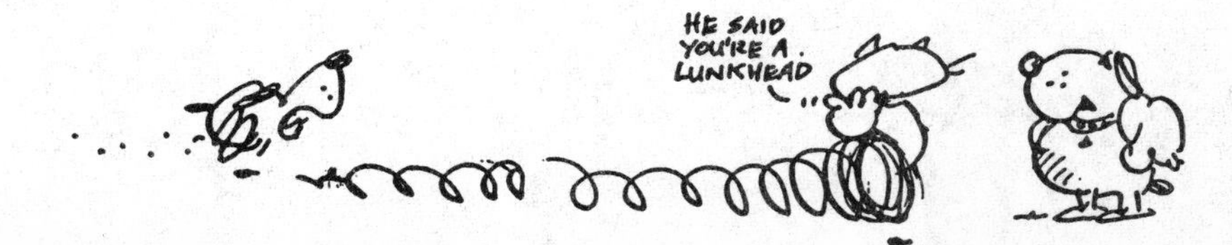
HE SAID YOU'RE A LUNKHEAD

NOW HERE'S WITHERSPOON SERVING FOR THE MATCH...
BOUNCE BOUNCE BOUNCE BOUNCE BOUNCE BOUNCE...

TOSS....

KA-CHAW!

A SNEEZE FROM HER ROYAL HIGHNESS MOMENTARILY STOPS PLAY.
SNIF
PETER PLANT

DID YOU KNOW I DO IMITATIONS OF FAMOUS PEOPLE, BOG'?
NO KIDDIN,' BERNIE.

SURE, LISTEN TO THIS... WHACK-ZIZZZ!
NICK FALDO TEEING OFF.
WHO WAS THAT?

HOW ABOUT THIS... TING-A-LING!
FRANK SINATRA WALKING INTO A NEWSAGENT'S.
WHO WAS THAT?

CAN YOU DO MERYL STREEP EATING A WATER-MELON?
I'M WORKING ON IT.
PETER PLANT

OUR 'CAT OF THE YEAR' AWARD GOES TO CHIPS, THE HATHAWAYS' CAT, WHO SAVED MRS. HATHAWAY'S LIFE BY WARNING HER ABOUT A ROLLER SKATE AT THE TOP OF THE STAIRS....

MRS. HATHAWAY TOLD US IT'S A COMPLETE MYSTERY AS TO HOW THE SKATE GOT THERE!...HERE'S A PHOTO OF THE HATHAWAYS WITH CHIPS!

PETER PLANT

Z

Z

BOO!
KIII

I HATE MYSELF FOR DOING THAT BUT THE LITTLE TYKE LOOKED LIKE HE COULD USE SOME EXERCISE.
YAP YAP YAP
SCRAMBLE THUD
SCRAMBLE
THUNK
THUD
YAP
YIP
PETER PLANT

NO, QUINCE! LEAVE IT! IT'S ANOTHER–
ZAP

MOTH.
BLECH! YAGH! PTOO! BLAGH! YECH!
PETER PLANT

AS SOCIAL CONVENOR, I NOTE THE DISCREPANCY IN THE RATIO OF GIRLS TO GUYS ATTENDING OUR SUMMER 'FROLIC', SIR.
LOYAL ORDER OF ELUSIVE BEAVERS

HOW MANY GIRLS HAVE WE GOT?
A HUNDRED AND FORTY-SIX, SIR.
AND HOW MANY GUYS?
EIGHT.

HMMM.
PETER PLANT

IT'S NOT THAT SERIOUS A DISCREPANCY, IS IT.
NOT REALLY.

DOG AHEAD

BILL AND EDITH, YOU'VE WON FIVE HUNDRED POUNDS HERE ON 'YOU BET YOUR BUTT'! DO YOU WANT TO HOLD ON TO IT, OR BET IT ALL ON WHAT'S INSIDE THIS ENVELOPE?

ER, NO, BOB. IT'S JUST ENOUGH TO PAY FOR EDITH'S OPERATION. WE'LL HOLD ON TO IT, THANKS.

AWW, G'WANN! THERE COULD BE A CHEQUE FOR A HUNDRED GRAND IN HERE!!
GO FOR IT! GO FOR IT! GO FOR IT!
WAVE WAVE

ER, OKAY BOB. WE'LL TAKE THE CHANCE.... WE'LL GO FOR IT....
RRRRIP

IT'S A DEAD MOTH! SORRY, BILL AND EDITH!
WHAT A RUTHLESS SHOW.
PETER PLANT

WHEN LITTLE GINNY FINDERFAST IS OUT ON THE TENNIS COURT HER MUM IS ALWAYS IN THE CROWD....
COME ON, BABY! YOU CAN DO IT!
RUN RUN RUN RUN

WATCHING AND CHEERING HER ON....
GO FOR IT, BABY! JUST GO FOR IT!
DASH DASH DASH DASH

WHICH SHOWS INCREDIBLE SUPPORT AND DEDICATION...
OOOOH! SHE MISSED IT!
SLAP
TRIP...
OOF!

CONSIDERING LITTLE GINNY IS ONLY A BALL-GIRL.
YYYES! SHE GOT ONE!
GRAB
PETER PLANT

CHATTER
CHATTER
CHATTER

CHATTER
CHATTER
CHATTER

CHATTER
CHATTER
CHATTER

OI! SHUT UP OUT THERE!
QUIET!
KEEP THE NOISE DOWN!
CHATTER
CHATTER
CHATTER

THERE'S NOTHING MORE ANNOYING THAN A CAT FOOLING AROUND ON A DIVING BOARD AT THREE A.M.
SLAM!
SLAM!
SLAM!
CHATTER
CHATTER
CHATTER
PETER PLANT

CAB!
RRRRRRRR

I DON'T UNDERSTAND IT, BOGART...

WHAT IS IT YOU FIND SO FASCINATING ABOUT THIS STUPID CRICKET?

WELL, ROZ, Y'SEE IT'S LIKE THIS...

HE SINGS, HE DANCES, AND HE TELLS PINOCCHIO NOT TO TELL LIES.
GIVVA LITTLE WHISTLE
PETER PLANT

...AND TO CONCLUDE OUR STUDY OF THE REPRODUCTIVE SYSTEM, GENTLEMEN, LET ME SAY THAT IT IS BIOLOGICALLY IMPOSSIBLE FOR A MALE PIGEON TO LAY AN EGG.

BOO.
YAAAA AAAAK!

PETER PLANT